Contents

Thanks are due to the following publishers for permission to reprint extracts from copyright works: Boosey & Hawkes Music Publishers Ltd; Breitkopf & Härtel; Editions Choudens/Cinephonic Music Co. Ltd; Consolidated Music Publishers/Dorsey Brothers Music Ltd; Novello & Co. Ltd; Oxford University Press; Theodore Presser Co.

The music on the cover is the opening of an arrangement for trumpet in D and piano by Philip Cranmer of the aria, 'The trumpet shall sound', from Handel's *Messiah* (*Handel and Bach Arias*, published by the Associated Board)

In the quoted music examples, tempo marks without brackets occur in the original as shown. Tempo marks in brackets occur earlier in the music or are editorial.

Music Theory in Practice

Grade 3

ERIC TAYLOR

The Associated Board of the Royal Schools of Music

Syllabus for Grade 3

As in preceding grades, with the addition of:

(1) Compound time signatures of $\frac{6}{8}$ $\frac{9}{8}$ $\frac{12}{8}$, and the grouping of notes and rests within these times. The demisemiquaver (32nd note) and its equivalent rest. Questions will include the composition of a simple four-bar rhythm which may start on an up-beat.

(2) Extension of the stave beyond two ledger lines. The transposition of a simple melody from the treble clef to the bass clef, or vice versa, at the octave.

(3) Scales and key signatures of all major and minor keys up to four sharps and flats, including both harmonic and melodic forms of minor scales, with their tonic triads (root position), degrees (number only), and intervals above the tonic (number and type).

(4) More terms and signs. The simple questions about a melody may include one on its phrase structure.

First published in 1990 by
The Associated Board of the Royal Schools of Music (Publishing) Ltd

Reprinted in 1990, 1991, 1992, 1994, 1995, 1997, 1998, 2000, 2001, 2002

ISBN 1 85472 492 4

Typesetting and music processing by Halstan & Co. Ltd, Amersham, Bucks
Printed in Great Britain by Headley Brothers Ltd, Ashford, Kent

A Demisemiquavers

(see *The AB Guide to Music Theory*, 1/1, 3/1 & 5/1–2)

The shortest note used in Grades 1 and 2 was the semiquaver.
In Grade 3, a note only *half* the length of a semiquaver is introduced:
the demisemiquaver 𝅘𝅥𝅰, with its equivalent rest 𝄿.

Exercise 1 Complete the following sentences by adding the right number on each of the dotted lines.

A 𝅘𝅥𝅯 lasts as long as . . . . 𝅘𝅥𝅰 s.

A 𝅘𝅥 lasts as long as . . . . 𝅘𝅥𝅰 s.

A 𝅘𝅥𝅮 lasts as long as . . . . 𝅘𝅥𝅰 s.

A 𝅝 lasts as long as . . . . 𝅘𝅥𝅰 s.

A 𝅘𝅥𝅮. lasts as long as . . . . 𝅘𝅥𝅰 s.

A 𝅗𝅥. lasts as long as . . . . 𝅘𝅥𝅰 s.

A 𝅘𝅥. lasts as long as . . . . 𝅘𝅥𝅰 s.

Exercise 2 Add the missing bar-lines in the following. They all begin on the first beat of the bar.

Exercise 3 Add the rest or rests needed at each of the places marked *.

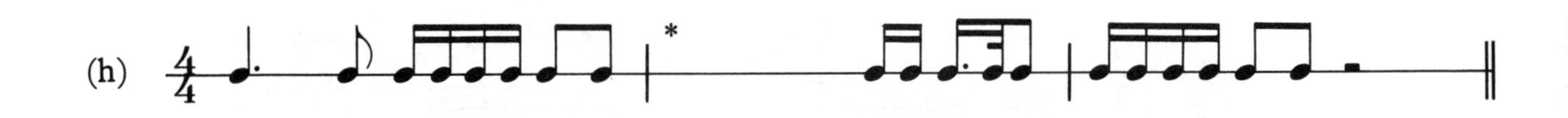

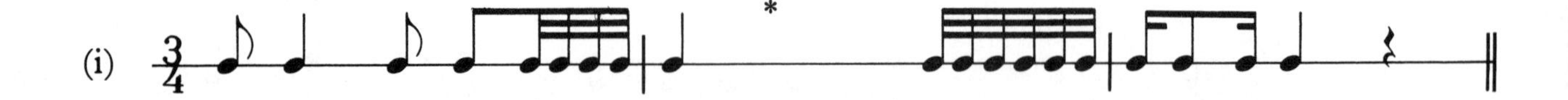

B Major keys with four sharps or flats

(see *The AB Guide to Music Theory*, 4/1)

The new major keys in this grade are E (four sharps) and A flat (four flats). You will be expected to know their scales, key signatures and tonic triads. You can easily work out these new scales if you keep in mind the pattern of tones and semitones in the major scale (TTS TTTS). Remember that the semitones always occur between the 3rd–4th and 7th–8th degrees of the scale.

Exercise 4 Write accidentals where they are needed to make the given scales. (Do not use key signatures.) Draw ⌐¬ over each pair of notes making a semitone.

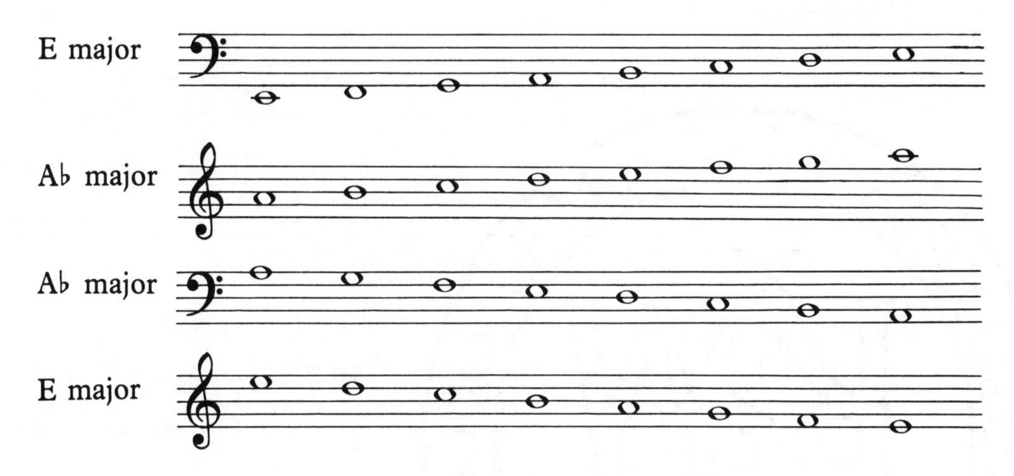

Exercise 5 After each of these clefs write the given key signature, followed by the tonic triad.

Exercise 6 Put the following into the given keys by writing accidentals before the notes which need them.

Exercise 7 Name the key of each of the following. Then write them out again, but using key signatures instead of accidentals.

C Beyond two ledger lines

Grade 3 exercises may use ledger lines beyond the two which were the limit in Grade 2.

Exercise 8 Underneath each of these notes write its letter name.

Exercise 9 Rewrite each of the following in the given clef, but at the same pitch.
(As an illustration, the answer to the opening of the first example is shown.)

D Transposition

(see *The AB Guide to Music Theory*, 7/2)

The easiest kind of transposition is introduced in Grade 3: transposing notes up or down an octave. You may be asked to write a melody in the treble clef an octave lower in the bass clef, or to write a melody in the bass clef an octave higher in the treble clef. There should be no difficulty, but careless mistakes sometimes occur. Apart from miscopying individual notes, there are two common errors. The first is to transpose the melody *two* octaves rather than one: for example,

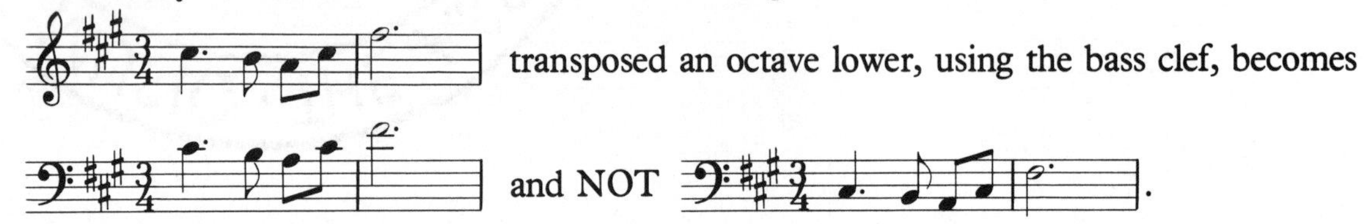

The other mistake is to write the melody at the *same* pitch, though using the other clef:

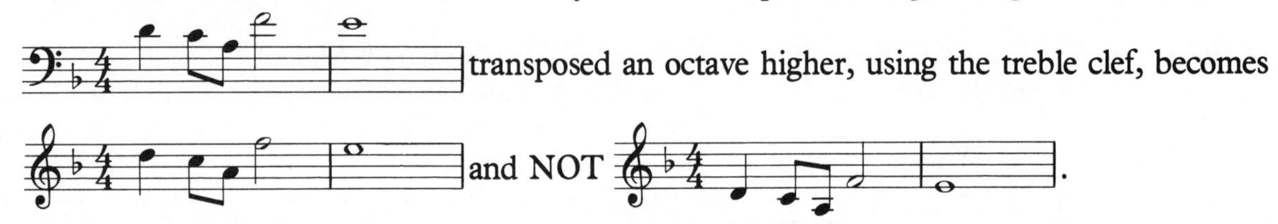

Exercise 10 Write each of these melodies an octave lower in the bass clef.

Exercise 11 Write each of these melodies an octave higher in the treble clef.

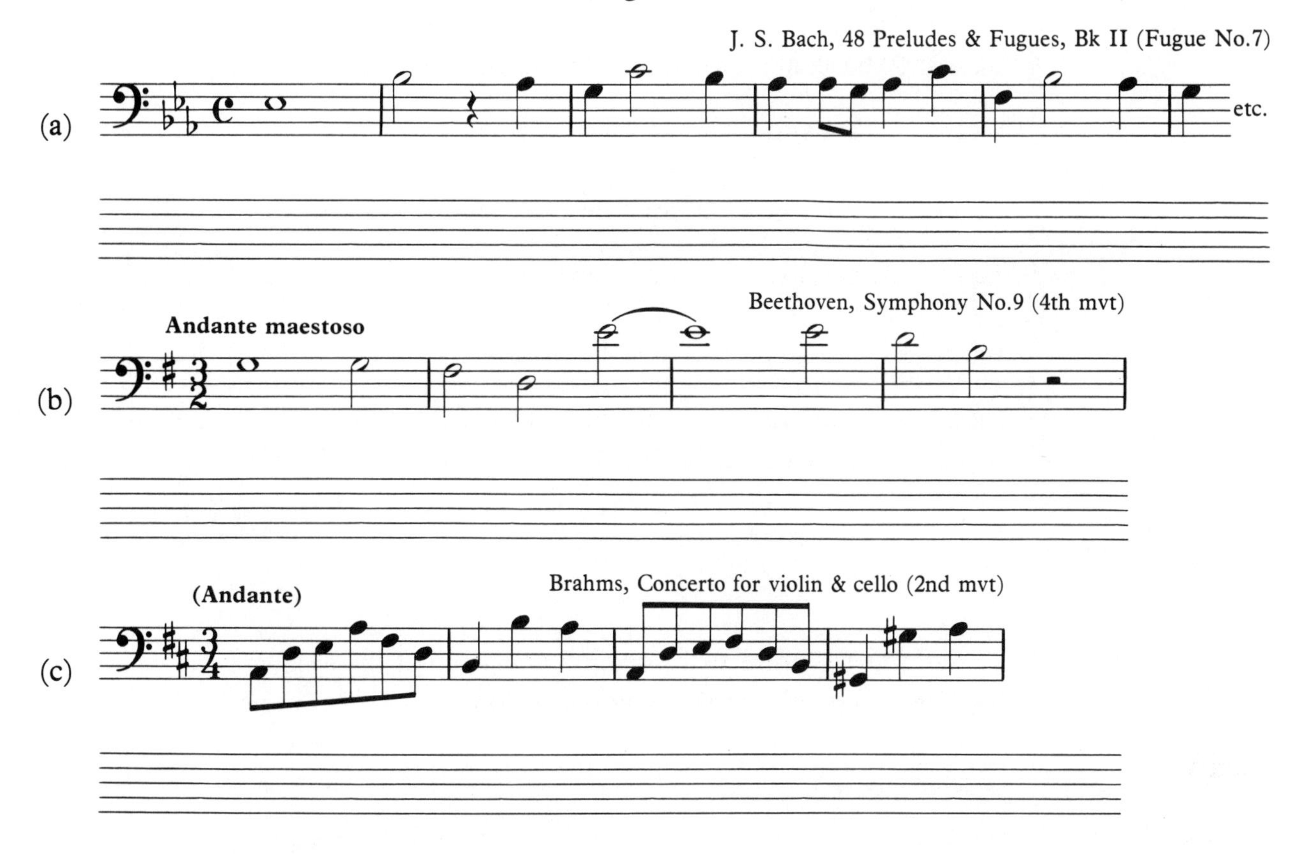

E Compound time

(see *The AB Guide to Music Theory*, 3/3–4)

All the time signatures which we have used so far have been examples of 'simple time'. This means that the beats can be divided into twos. A ♩ beat (as in $\frac{2}{4}$, $\frac{3}{4}$ or $\frac{4}{4}$), for example, can be divided into ♫ . Similarly, a 𝅗𝅥 beat (as in $\frac{2}{2}$, $\frac{3}{2}$ or $\frac{4}{2}$) can be divided into ♩ ♩ ; or a ♪ beat ($\frac{3}{8}$) into ♬ .

There is another kind of time: 'compound time'. In compound time the beats divide into threes. When they are written down, the beats are written as *dotted* notes: for example, ♩. , which can be divided into ♪♪♪ . In Grade 3, all the compound time signatures will take a dotted crotchet (♩.) as the sign for one beat. Three time signatures will be used:

$\frac{6}{8}$, meaning 2 dotted crotchet beats in a bar;
$\frac{9}{8}$, meaning 3 dotted crotchet beats in a bar;
$\frac{12}{8}$, meaning 4 dotted crotchet beats in a bar.

When a ♩. is divided into three quavers, they are joined ('beamed') together in threes:

$\frac{6}{8}$ ♪♪♪ ♪♪♪ | $\frac{9}{8}$ ♪♪♪ ♪♪♪ ♪♪♪ | $\frac{12}{8}$ ♪♪♪ ♪♪♪ ♪♪♪ ♪♪♪ |

More will be said about the grouping of notes and rests in Section G.

Exercise 12 The first of the following sentences is given in full. Complete the others by filling the gaps.

$\frac{2}{4}$ means 2 beats in a bar, and the beats are crotchets.

$\frac{6}{8}$ means . . . beats in a bar, and the beats are . . . .

$\frac{3}{4}$ means . . . beats in a bar, and the beats are . . . .

$\frac{9}{8}$ means . . . beats in a bar, and the beats are . . . .

$\frac{4}{4}$ means . . . beats in a bar, and the beats are . . . .

$\frac{12}{8}$ means . . . beats in a bar, and the beats are . . . .

Exercise 13 Write the time signature at the beginning of each of the following bars, and add either 'simple' or 'compound' in the sentences below.

(a)

This is in . . . . time.

(b)

This is in . . . . time.

(c)

This is in . . . . time.

(d)

This is in . . . . time.

(e)

This is in . . . . time.

(f)

This is in . . . . time.

Notice that we can describe time signatures in two ways:

1) as duple, triple or quadruple,

2) as simple or compound.

So these are the full descriptions of the time signatures we have studied so far:

$\frac{2}{4}$, $\frac{2}{2}$ simple duple time	$\frac{6}{8}$ compound duple time
$\frac{3}{4}$, $\frac{3}{2}$, $\frac{3}{8}$ simple triple time	$\frac{9}{8}$ compound triple time
$\frac{4}{4}$, $\frac{4}{2}$ simple quadruple time	$\frac{12}{8}$ compound quadruple time

Exercise 14 Add the time signature at the beginning of each of the following, and describe the kind of time by completing the sentences below. (The answer to (a) is given in full as an example.)

Exercise 15 Add the missing bar-lines in the following. They all begin on the first beat of the bar.

Exercise 16 At each of the places marked * add one rest (with a dot, if needed).

You will remember from Grade 2 that, even in simple time, a beat can be divided into three by writing a triplet. So these examples sound exactly the same:

Simple time signatures are chosen when the beats normally divide into twos. Compound time signatures are chosen when the beats normally divide into threes. But it is always *possible* to write a piece of music using *either* a simple *or* a compound time signature without altering its sound.

Exercise 17 The examples (a) and (b) below show how a melody in simple time may be written in compound time (and vice versa) without altering its sound. In the same way, rewrite the remaining melodies in the given time signatures.

Exercise 17
(continued)

F Minor keys with four sharps or flats

(see *The AB Guide to Music Theory*, 4/2–3)

In Grade 2 you were given the choice of using either the harmonic or the melodic form of the minor scales. In Grade 3, however, you will be expected to know *both* forms of the minor scales set for the grade, including those which were set in Grade 2 (A minor, E minor, D minor). The next two exercises, therefore, provide practice in using both forms of these three Grade 2 scales before the new keys for Grade 3 are introduced.

Exercise 18 Write in accidentals where they are needed to make the scales named. (Do not use key signatures.) Draw ⌐¬ over each pair of notes making a semitone.

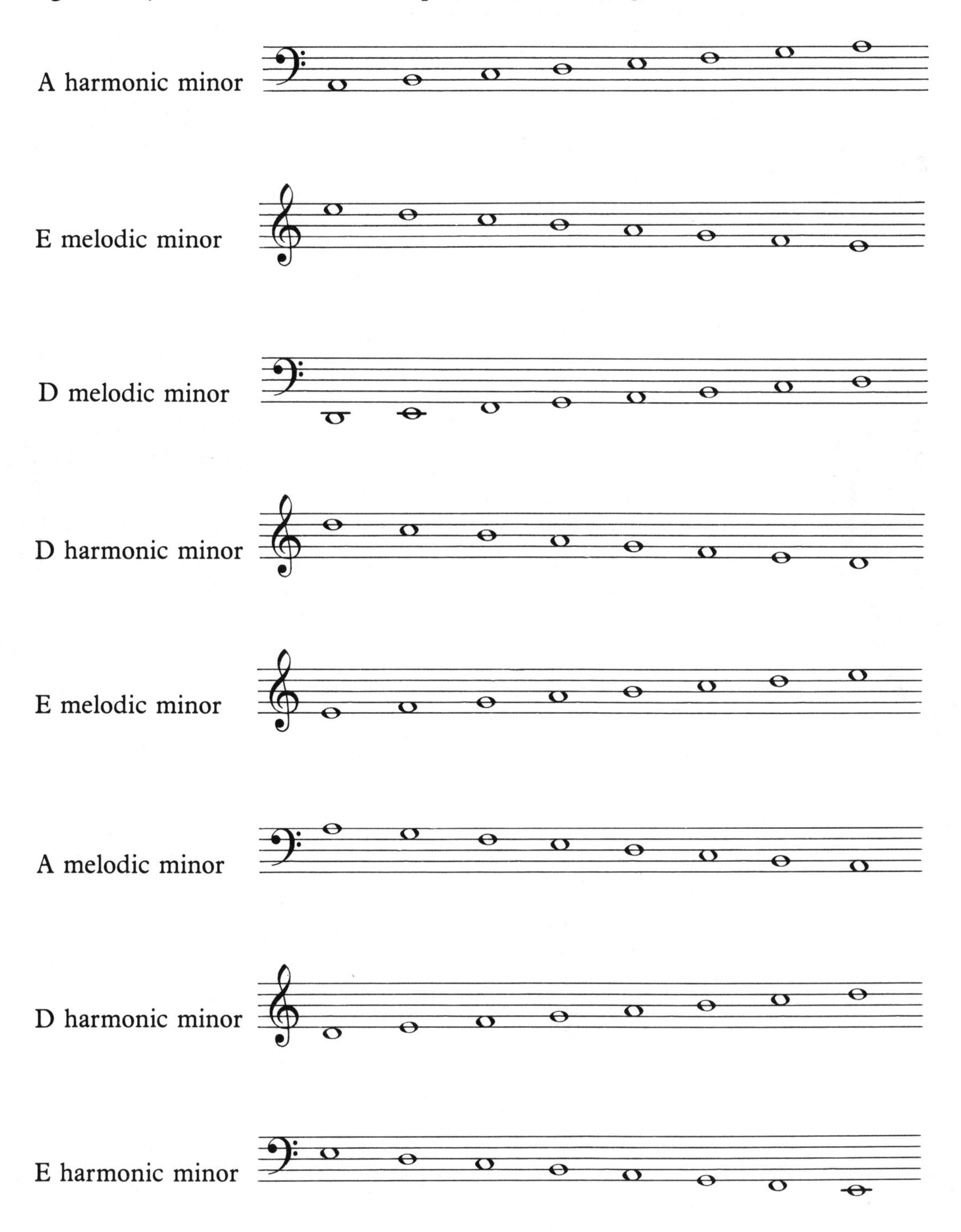

Exercise 19 Write the scales named below, using the given rhythms. Add the appropriate key signatures, but do not use any unnecessary accidentals.

The new minor keys for Grade 3 are: B minor (two sharps in the key signature), F♯ minor (three sharps) and C♯ minor (four sharps); G minor (two flats), C minor (three flats) and F minor (four flats). The scales of these keys are shown in both the harmonic and melodic forms in Exercise 20 below. Remember that the harmonic form always uses the same notes descending as ascending.

Exercise 20 In these scales, draw ⌐¬ above any pairs of notes which are a semitone apart.

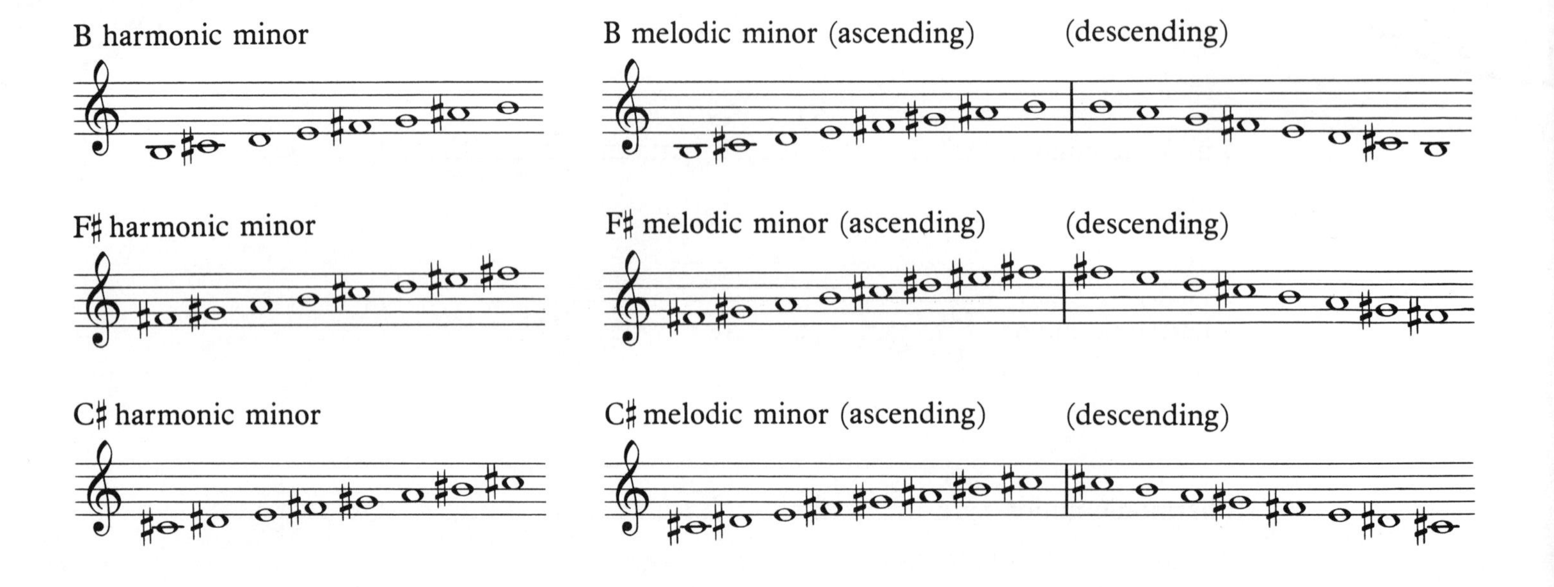

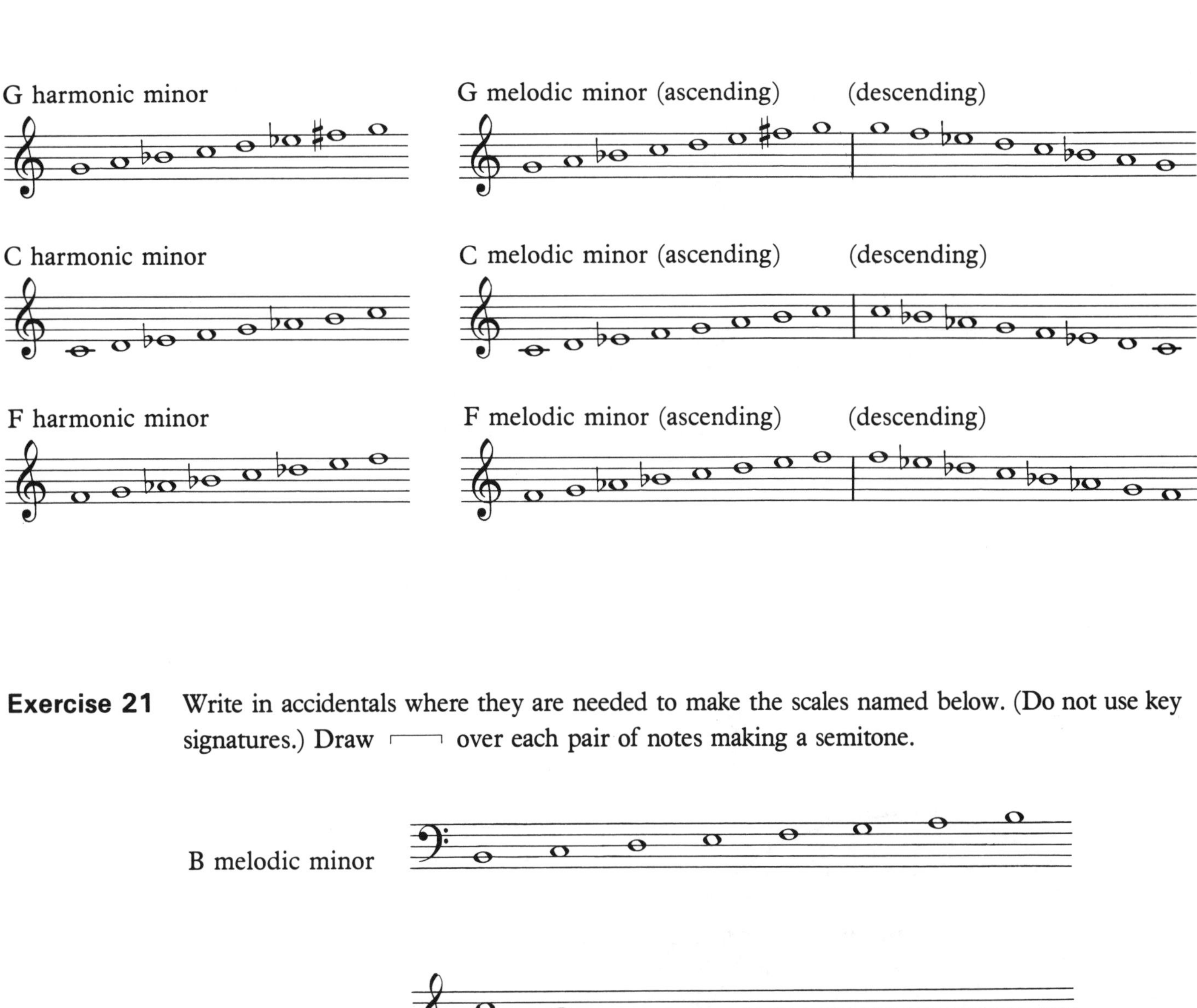

Exercise 21 Write in accidentals where they are needed to make the scales named below. (Do not use key signatures.) Draw ⌐¬ over each pair of notes making a semitone.

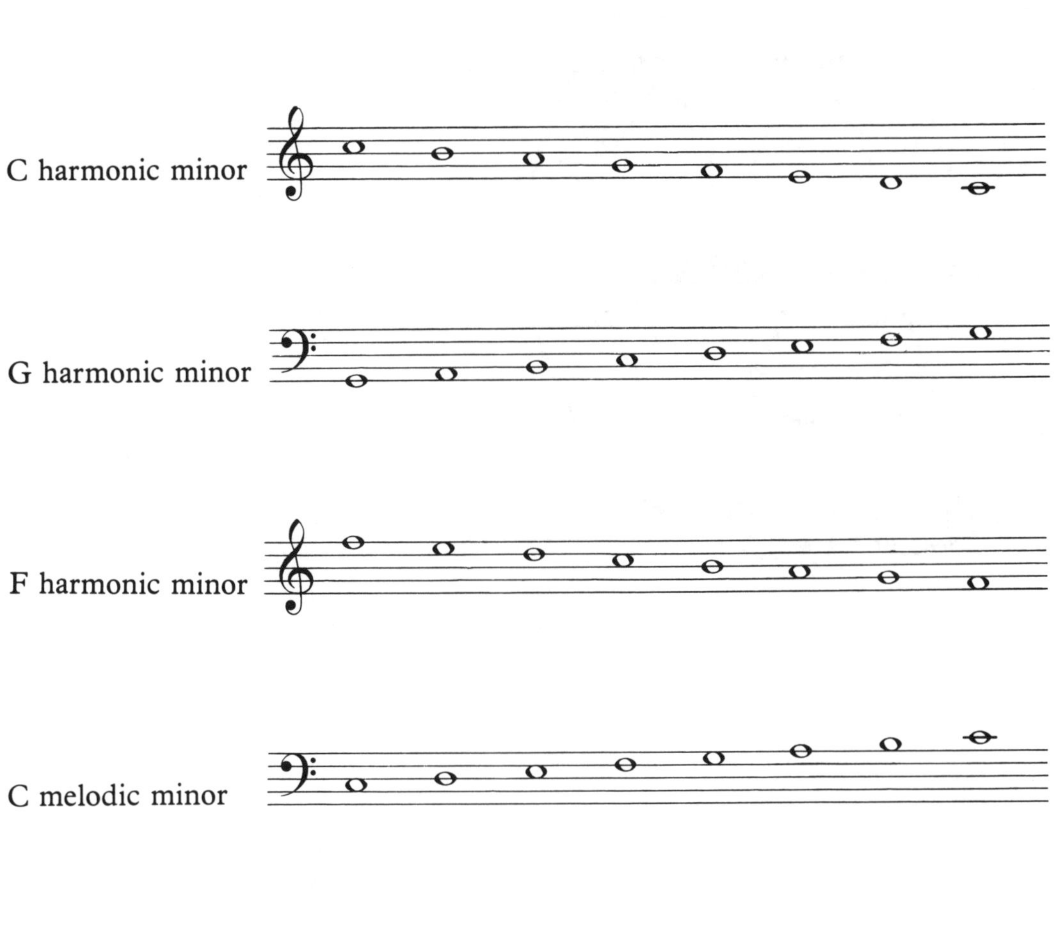

Exercise 22 After each of these clefs write the given key signature, followed by the tonic triad.

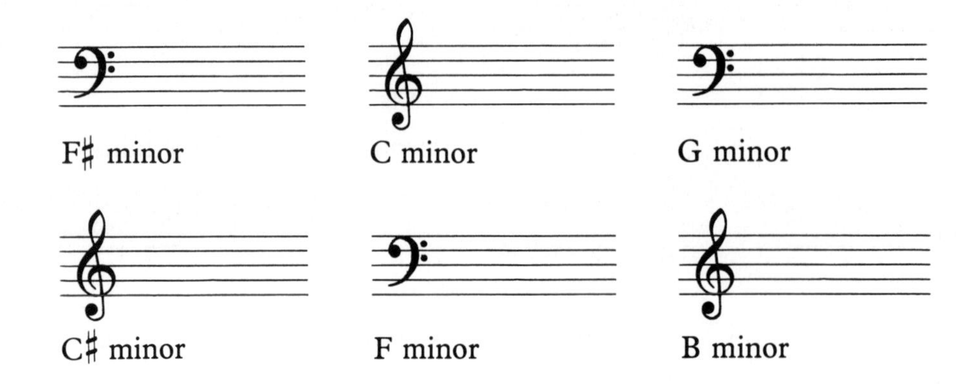

Exercise 23 After each of the following clefs write the given key signature. Then write the scale in the form shown, using the given rhythm. Do not use any unnecessary accidentals.

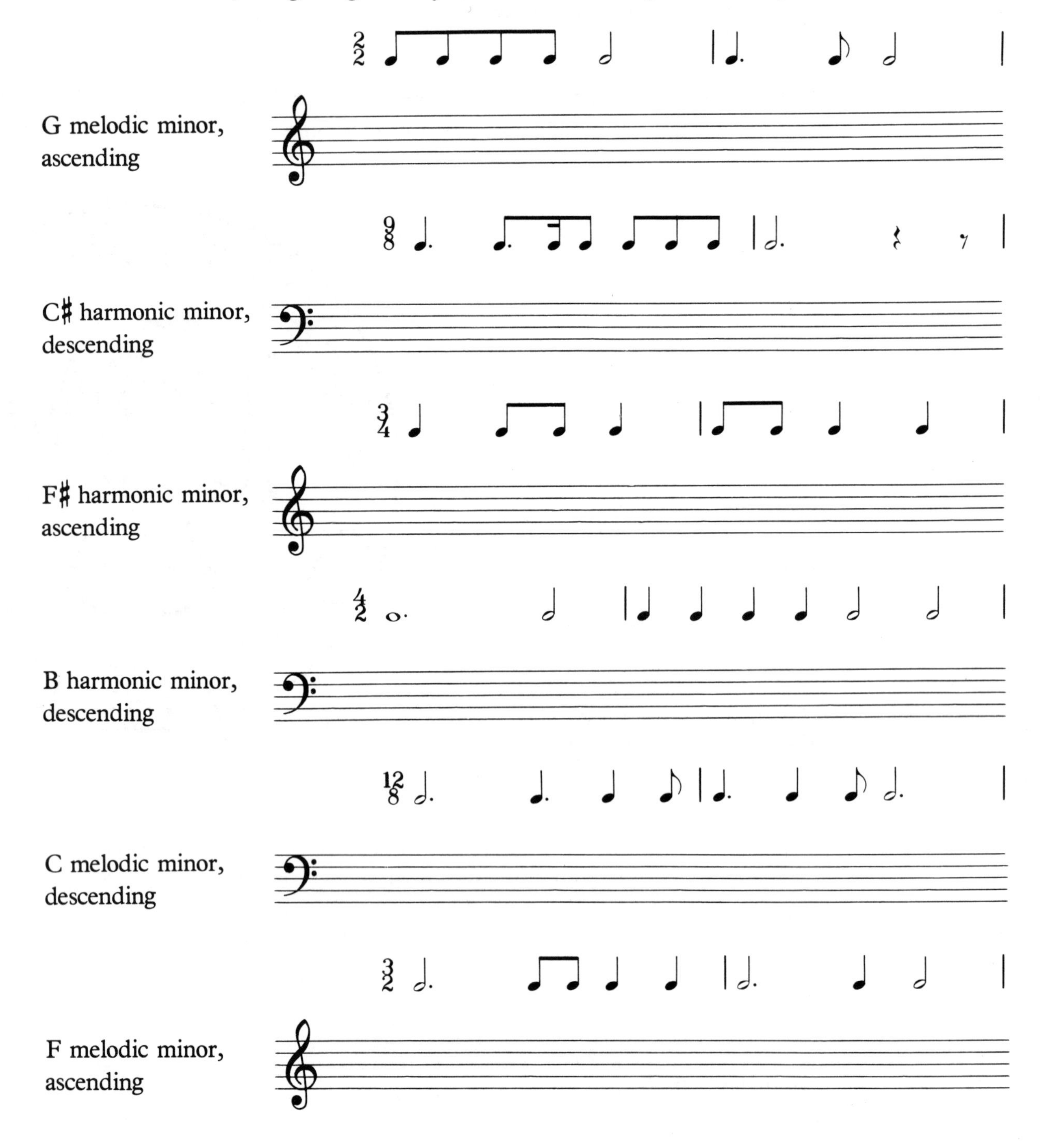

G Grouping notes and rests in compound time

(see *The AB Guide to Music Theory*, 5/1–2)

In Section E we saw how notes making up a beat in compound time are beamed together:

A single beat may be divided into or (not or).

Notice that $\frac{6}{8}$ (above) was not written . (Six quavers beamed together would imply $\frac{3}{4}$.) However, since the beaming of the notes shows where the beats begin, ties sometimes have to be used: $\frac{6}{8}$ (not , again implying $\frac{3}{4}$).

Semiquavers as well as quavers (and mixtures of the two) are also beamed together in beats:

But in $\frac{6}{8}$, $\frac{9}{8}$ and $\frac{12}{8}$, notes lasting two full beats are written (not).
A note lasting a full bar is written in $\frac{9}{8}$, and in $\frac{12}{8}$.

A one-beat rest in $\frac{6}{8}$, $\frac{9}{8}$ or $\frac{12}{8}$ may be written either or . As in simple time, a new beat needs a new rest. For example, there are no correct alternatives to these:

(except that in every case may be replaced by). However, in $\frac{12}{8}$ a rest is used for the first two beats or for the last two: .
In all compound time signatures, a completely silent bar is shown (without a dot).

When a beat includes rests, they are arranged like this:
(was written in the past but is not normal now).
Remember that (with the exceptions mentioned above) a new beat needs a new rest:
(would imply $\frac{3}{4}$)

Semiquaver rests are used the same way as in simple time. In other words, a semiquaver rest is needed to 'finish off' the quaver before any other rest follows:
(not). In this next example, the semiquaver rest also follows the general rule that a new beat needs a new rest: .

Beams may be used across rests. For instance, shows clearly that the group makes up one compound time beat: and are not so clear.

Exercise 24 Rewrite the following melodies, grouping the notes and rests correctly.

H Scales and key signatures (further practice)

The following exercises are for general revision in scales and key signatures: they are based on all the work in scales and keys (both major and minor) covered so far, including those set in the earlier grades.

Exercise 25 Add the clefs and key signatures needed to make the given scales. In the case of minor scales, remember to add those accidentals which are necessary, but do not add any which are not.

Exercise 26 Name the key of each of the following. Then rewrite them, using the correct key signatures. Remove any accidentals which become unnecessary, but remember also to add any that may be needed.

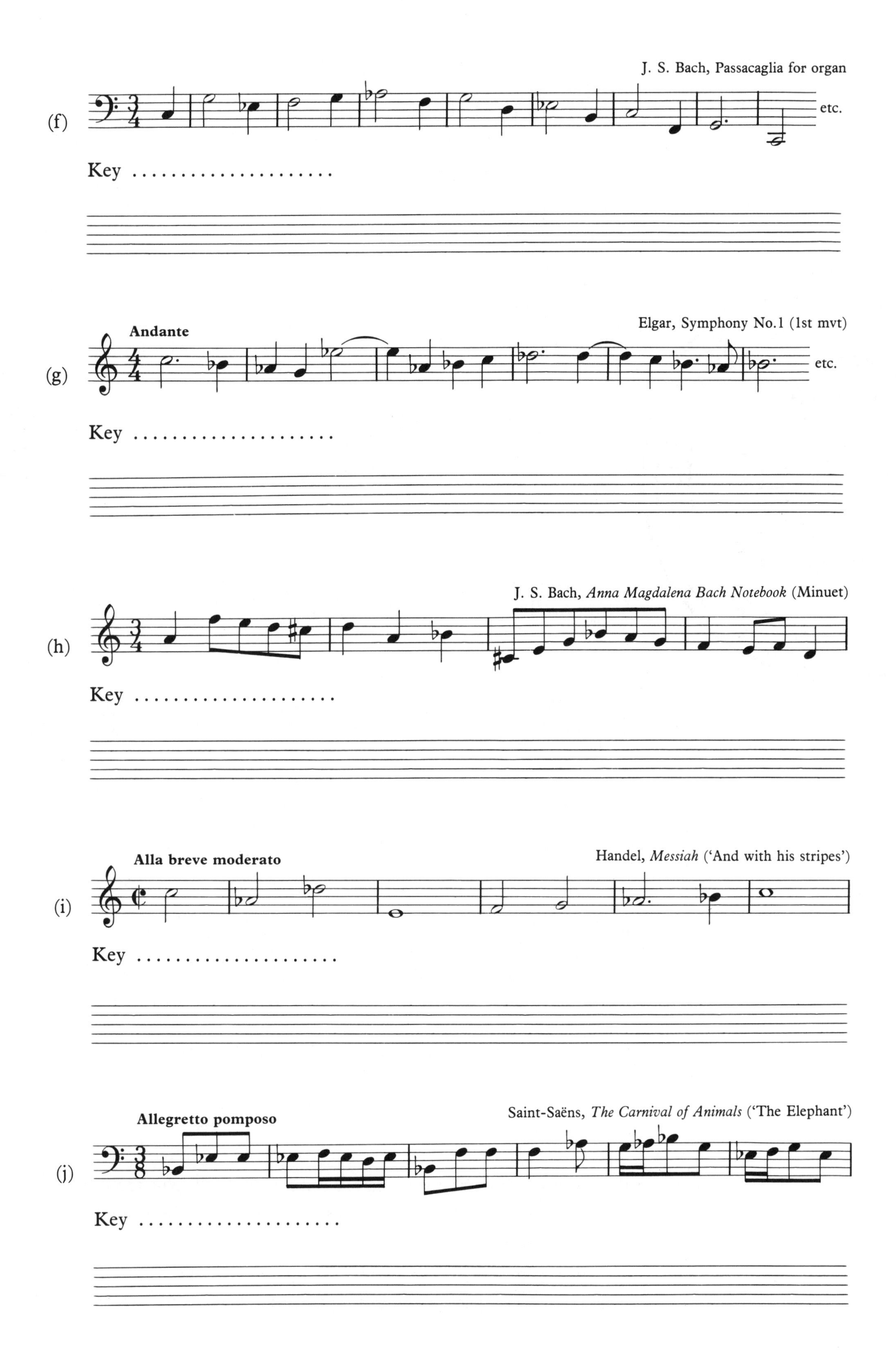
J. S. Bach, Passacaglia for organ
(f)
etc.
Key ....
Andante
Elgar, Symphony No.1 (1st mvt)
(g)
etc.
Key ....
J. S. Bach, *Anna Magdalena Bach Notebook* (Minuet)
(h)
Key ....
Alla breve moderato
Handel, *Messiah* ('And with his stripes')
(i)
Key ....
Allegretto pomposo
Saint-Saëns, *The Carnival of Animals* ('The Elephant')
(j)
Key ....

I Four-bar rhythms

The four-bar rhythms studied in Grade 2 all started on the first beat of a bar. Here are some which start *before* the first beat on bar 1 (remembering that bars are numbered from the first complete bar). This kind of opening is called an 'anacrusis'.

Notice in the examples above that the number of beats in bar 4, plus those before the first bar-line, add up to a full bar. A four-bar rhythm in $\frac{3}{4}$, for example, contains a total of 12 beats, irrespective of which beat it starts on. Similarly, one in $\frac{4}{4}$ contains 16 beats. This is by no means a rule, but it happens very often – particularly in simple songs, dances and marches.

Four-bar rhythms which start before the first bar-line are in all other ways similar to those studied in Grade 2. For instance, the examples on the opposite page show that the second half may be an exact repetition of the first half:

or the second half may be very nearly the same as the first –

or the two halves may just start similarly –

or there may be rhythmic repetitions used in other ways –

or there may be no repetitions at all –

Example (f) above shows a very common device, sometimes called the 'ready-steady-go' principle: a pattern is played three times, but with the third continuing.
Here is another example, from the slow movement of Beethoven's Violin Concerto:

In the following exercises, experiment in composing four-bar rhythms in different ways: some including repetitions of various kinds, and some without any.

Exercise 27 Compose four-bar rhythms beginning as follows.

(a)

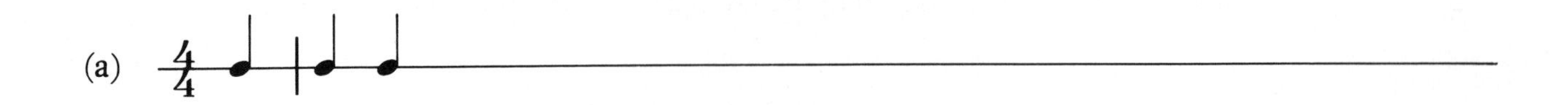

(b)

(c)

(d)

(e)

(f)

(g)

(h)

(i)

(j)

(k)

Exercise 28 Include each of the following in a four-bar rhythm, though not necessarily at the beginning.

(a)

(b)

(c)

(d)

(e)

(f)

(g)

(h)

J Intervals

(see *The AB Guide to Music Theory*, 7/1)

When you are asked to name an interval, you will have to give not only its number but also its type ('quality'). In Grade 3, the lower note of the interval will always be the key-note (tonic) of one of the major or minor scales set for this grade.

Remember that, in major scales, the interval between the key-note and the 4th and 5th degrees above is always 'perfect'. The key-note to its octave is also a perfect interval. The interval between the key-note and all other degrees is 'major': major 2nd, 3rd, 6th, 7th.

In minor keys, the situation is a little more complicated. The 4th and 5th degrees are the same as in the major scale, so these still produce perfect intervals, as does the octave. However, the interval between the key-note and the 3rd degree is different: it is a 'minor' 3rd. The 6th and 7th degrees of minor scales vary according to which kind of minor scale is being used (harmonic or melodic), and also whether it is ascending or descending. If the 6th and 7th degrees in a minor scale are the same as in a major scale, they still produce major intervals from the key-note. Otherwise they are minor.

This illustrates all the possibilities, with C as the key-note.

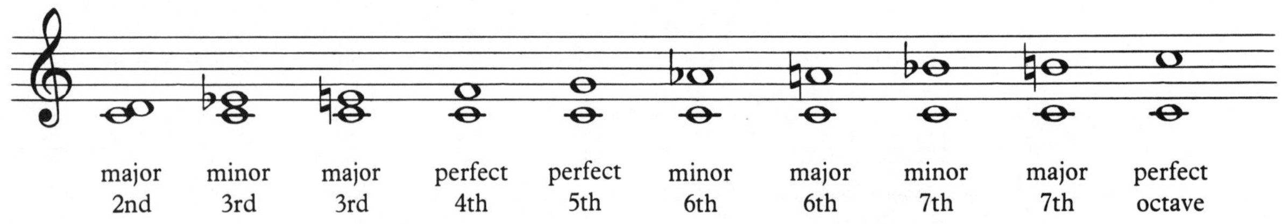

It does not matter which of the two notes of an interval is played first, or whether they are played together: the name of the interval remains the same.

Exercise 29 Underneath each of these intervals write its full name (e.g. minor 3rd, perfect 5th). In each case the lower note is the key-note – the 1st degree of the scale.

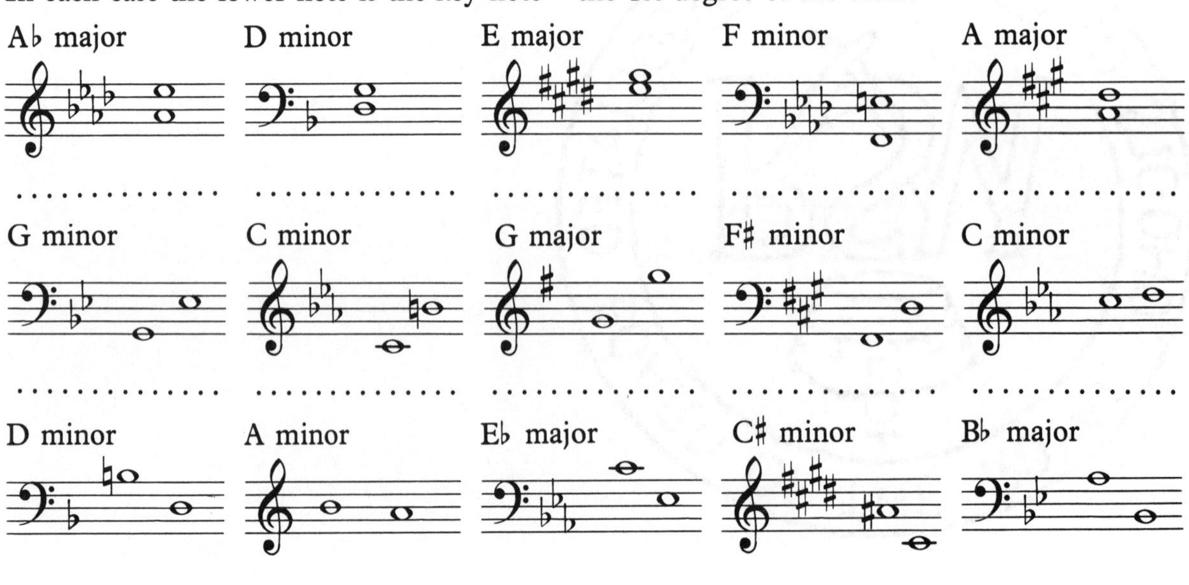

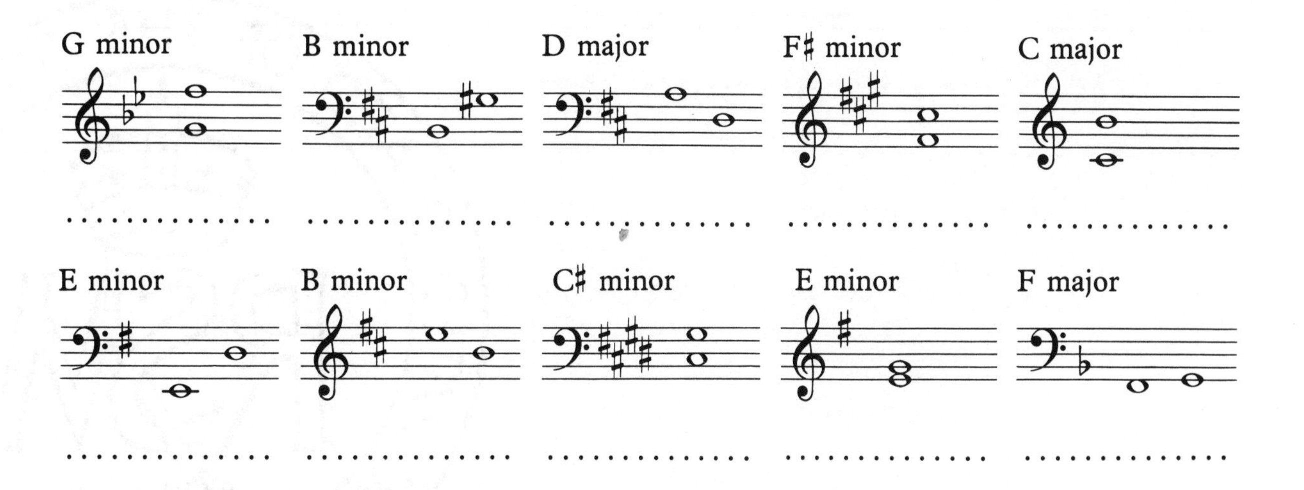

Exercise 30 Name the intervals between each pair of notes marked in the following. In each case, the lower note is the key-note of the melody.

K Simple phrase structure

(see *The AB Guide to Music Theory*, 9/1)

If you look carefully at the sentence you are reading now, you will see that it consists of two parts. The division into two parts is shown by the comma. Similarly, a poem is divided into verses, and the verses are divided into lines. A melody, too, can be divided up: it consists of sections called phrases.

Phrases are of many different kinds, and the phrase structure of a piece of music can be very complicated. In Grade 3, however, questions will be asked on only the most basic types of phrase. A particularly common type of melody is one consisting of four phrases: either four 2-bar phrases (making an 8-bar melody) or four 4-bar phrases (a 16-bar melody). Here, for example, is a familiar 16-bar passage (although not in this case the complete melody) consisting of four 4-bar phrases. To show them, square brackets ⌐¬ have been added above the stave:

Elgar, *Pomp and Circumstance* March No.1

Regular phrase patterns of this kind arise naturally when a verse is set to music:

Melody from Este's Psalter (1592)
Words by Nahum Tate

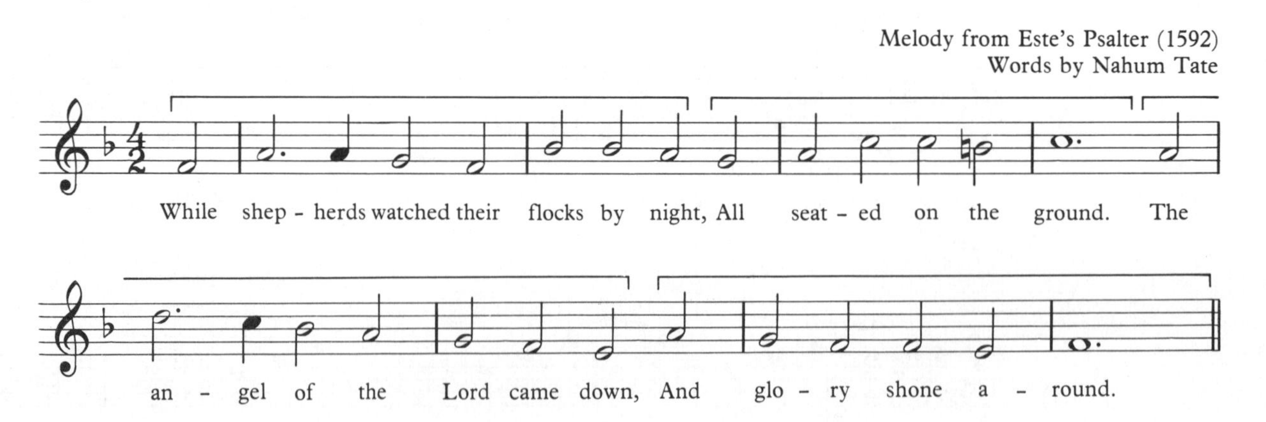

In the Elgar melody above, all the phrases begin on the first beat of a bar.
In 'While shepherds watched', however, they all begin on a minim *before* the bar-line.
Phrases can begin at any point in a bar. But wherever they begin, the phrases in a melody often start with the same rhythm, or with rhythms which are nearly the same.
For example, the Elgar phrases not only all begin on the first beat of a bar, they also start with a minim. Moreover, both of the first two phrases begin 𝅗𝅥 | ♫ ♩ |,
while both of the last two phrases begin 𝅗𝅥 | ♪♩ ♪|.

Repetitions or similarities of this kind provide a valuable clue in spotting how a melody is divided into phrases. Another clue, which may sometimes be found, is the use of longer notes at the ends of phrases. The endings of all the phrases in this melody provide examples.

In this last example, the first, second and fourth phrases are almost identical in notes as well as in rhythm. This makes the division of the melody into phrases particularly easy to see. The best guide, however, is not what the music *looks* like on paper but how it *sounds*, so it is important to try and 'hear' the melody in your head. When you are practising, of course, you can actually play it, or sing it aloud. In the examination room, even if you cannot be sure of 'hearing' the exact pitch of the notes, try at least to imagine the rhythm correctly. Fortunately, rhythm is nearly always the best single guide to phrase structure.

Two more introductory points need to be made:

(1) Although 2-, 4- and 8-bar phrases are by far the most common, others may be found. The Minuet in Mozart's Symphony No.40 (in G minor), for example, begins with two 3-bar phrases:

(2) In all the above examples, phrases have been shown by ┌──┐ signs. They are deliberately used here because they are not used in real music: thus it is easy to see what the composer wrote and what has been added simply for study purposes. In real music, signs are used not to show where phrases begin and end, but how they are to be *performed* - in detail. Thus composers may use staccato dots (to show that the notes are to be detached), slurs (to show that they are to be played smoothly), and other such signs.

Here, for example, are the first eight bars of a piece for piano as the composer wrote them:

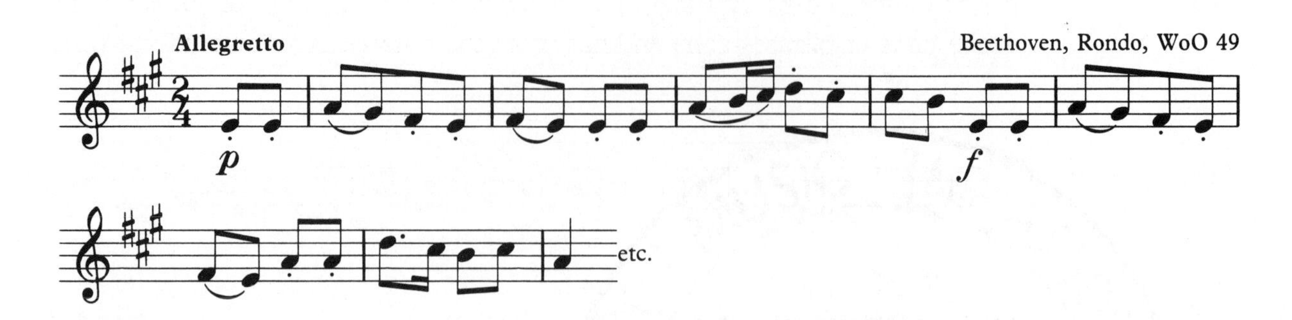

Here they are again, with square brackets added to show the phrases:

That is why it is misleading to describe slurs, staccato dots, etc. as 'phrasing marks', although the expression is commonly used. They are better called 'articulation marks'.

Exercise 31 Add ⌐¬ marks to show the phrases in each of the following. (The first phrase is already marked in (a), (b) and (c); in the remaining examples other phrases are marked.)

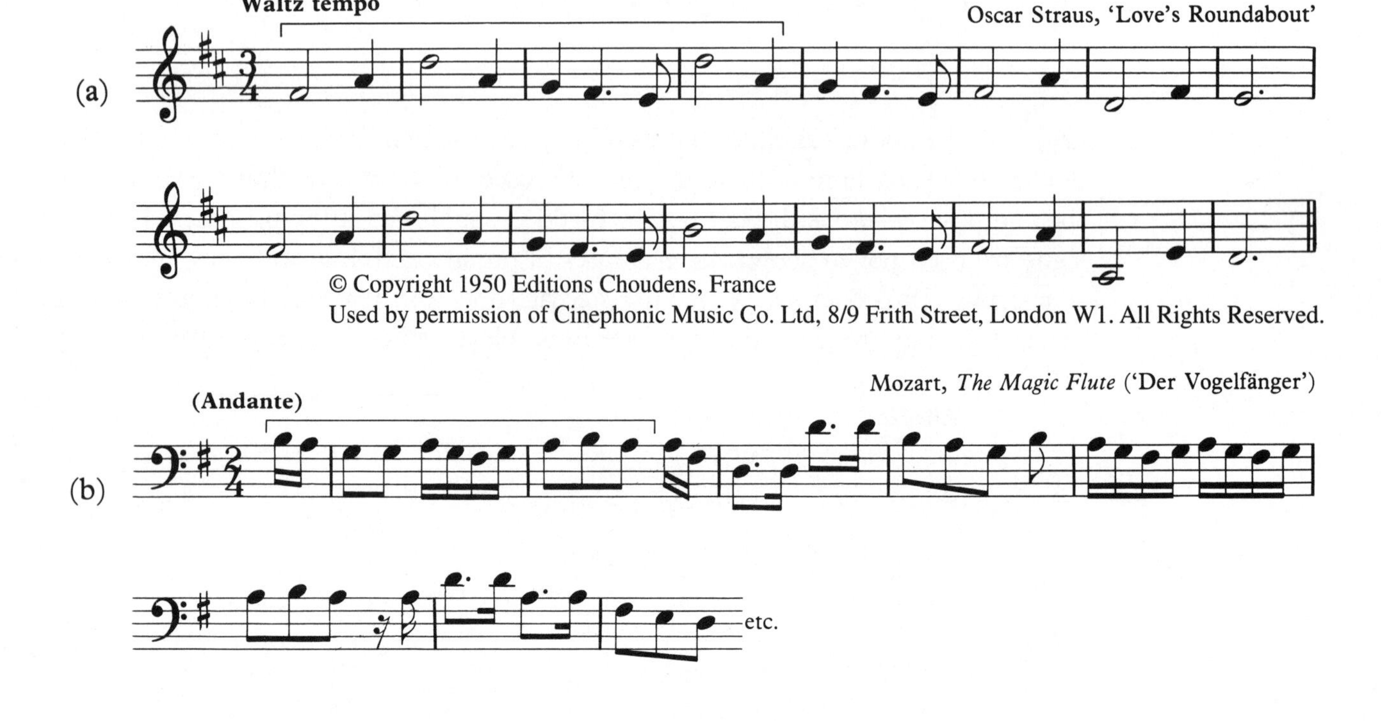

Purcell, 'Rejoice in the Lord alway'
(c)
Lento molto espressivo
Walford Davies, *Solemn Melody*
(d)
p
Reproduced by permission of Novello & Co. Ltd.
J. S. Bach, French Suite No.6 (Gavotte)
(e)
(Allegro)
Folksong, 'The Coasts of High Barbary'
(f)
Allegro
Mozart, Concerto for two pianos (3rd mvt)
(g)

L Performance directions

(see *The AB Guide to Music Theory*, 10 and 11)

Here are some words (in addition to those in earlier grades) – all Italian – which you will be expected to know in Grade 3.

adagietto	rather slow (but faster than *adagio*)
ad libitum, ad lib.	at choice, meaning that a passage may be played freely
agitato	agitated
alla breve	with a minim beat, equivalent to 𝄵 ($\frac{2}{2}$), implying a faster tempo than the note values might otherwise suggest
amore	love (*amoroso*: loving)
anima	soul, spirit (*con anima* can mean 'with feeling' or 'spirited')
animato	animated, lively (*animando*: becoming more lively)
ben	well
brio	vigour (*con brio*: with vigour, lively)
comodo	convenient (*tempo comodo*: at a comfortable speed)
deciso	with determination
delicato	delicate
energico	energetic
forza	force
largamente	broadly
leggiero	light, nimble
marcato, marc.	emphatic, accented
marziale	in a military style
mesto	sad
pesante	heavy
prima, primo	first
risoluto	bold, strong
ritmico	rhythmically
rubato, tempo rubato	with some freedom of time
scherzando, scherzoso	playful, joking
seconda, secondo	second
semplice	simple, plain
sempre	always
stringendo	gradually getting faster
subito	suddenly
tanto	so much
tranquillo	calm
triste, tristamente	sad, sorrowful
volta	time (*prima volta*: first time; *seconda volta*: second time)

M General exercises

Exercise 32 This melody is played by cellos at the opening of the second movement of Beethoven's Fifth Symphony. Answer the questions below.

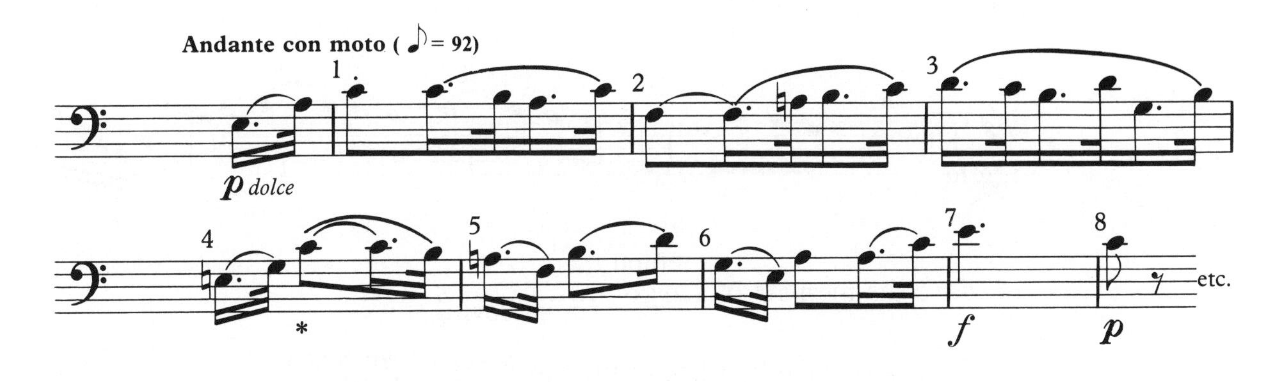

(a) The key is A♭ major. Add the key signature where required.

(b) Add the time signature where required.

(c) Which is the loudest note? .... in bar ....

(d) In which bar are notes tied? ....

(e) What do you notice about the highest and the lowest note?

....

(f) Give the meaning of:

(i) **Andante con moto** ....

(ii) ♪ = 92 ....

(iii) *dolce* ....

(g) Name the interval between the last two notes in bar 6 ....

(h) Draw a circle round three notes next to each other which belong to the tonic triad.

(i) Transpose the first four bars (as far as the note marked *) up an octave, writing in the treble clef.

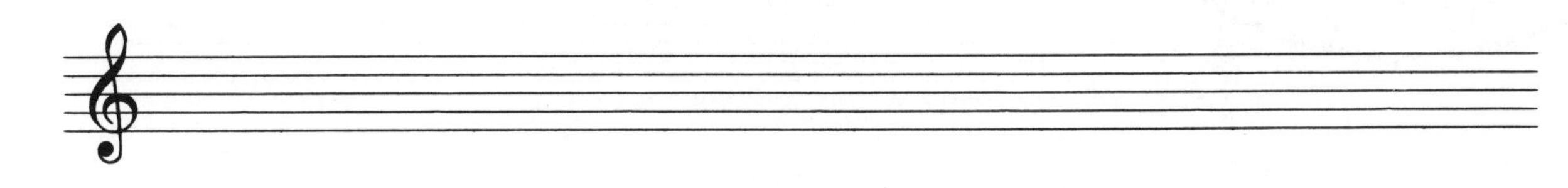

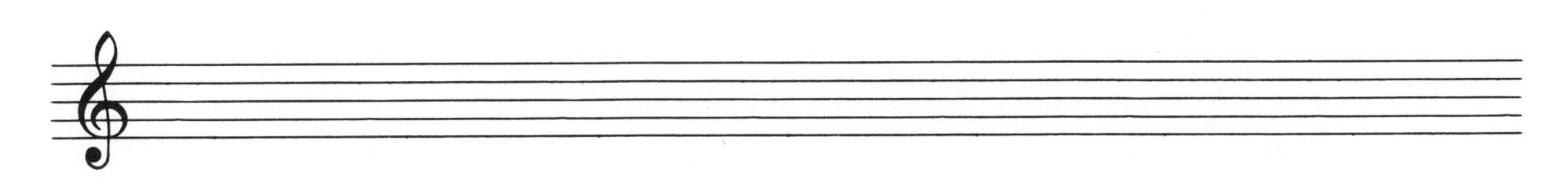

Exercise 33 Look at this passage, which is the opening of a Violin Sonata by Geminiani, and then answer the questions below.

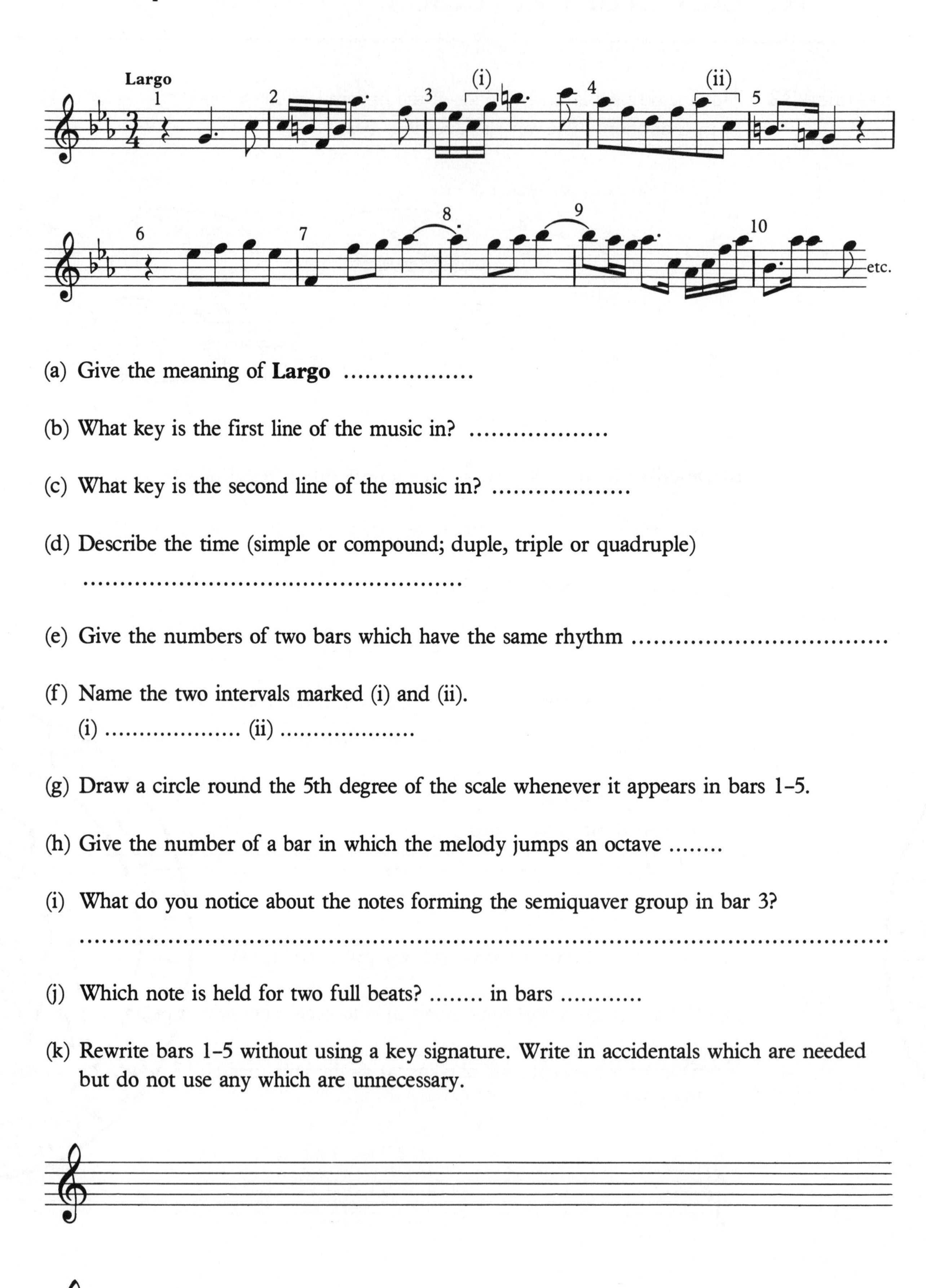

(a) Give the meaning of **Largo** ....

(b) What key is the first line of the music in? ....

(c) What key is the second line of the music in? ....

(d) Describe the time (simple or compound; duple, triple or quadruple)
....

(e) Give the numbers of two bars which have the same rhythm ....

(f) Name the two intervals marked (i) and (ii).
(i) .... (ii) ....

(g) Draw a circle round the 5th degree of the scale whenever it appears in bars 1–5.

(h) Give the number of a bar in which the melody jumps an octave ....

(i) What do you notice about the notes forming the semiquaver group in bar 3?
....

(j) Which note is held for two full beats? .... in bars ....

(k) Rewrite bars 1–5 without using a key signature. Write in accidentals which are needed but do not use any which are unnecessary.

Exercise 34 Look at this melody, which is the theme (composed by Henry Purcell) of Benjamin Britten's *Young Person's Guide to the Orchestra*, and then answer the questions below.

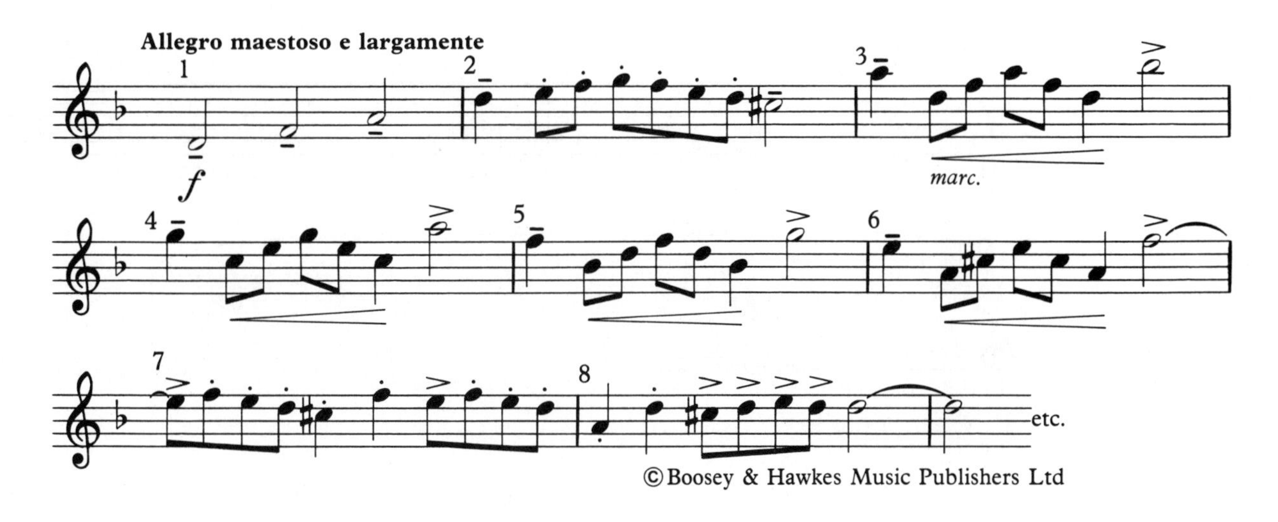

(a) Add the time signature where required.

(b) Describe the time (simple or compound; duple, triple or quadruple)

....

(c) Name the key ....

(d) Draw a circle round three notes next to each other which form the tonic triad.

(e) Which is the highest note? .... in bar ....

(f) What do you notice about bars 3, 4, 5 and 6?

....

(g) Give the meaning of the following:

(i) **Allegro maestoso e largamente** ....

(ii) *marc.* ....

(iii) – signs above or below notes ....

(iv) > signs above notes ....

(v) ⌒ over the last two minims ....

(h) Rewrite bars 1–3 in notes which are half as long (the first note is given). Remember to add the new time signature.

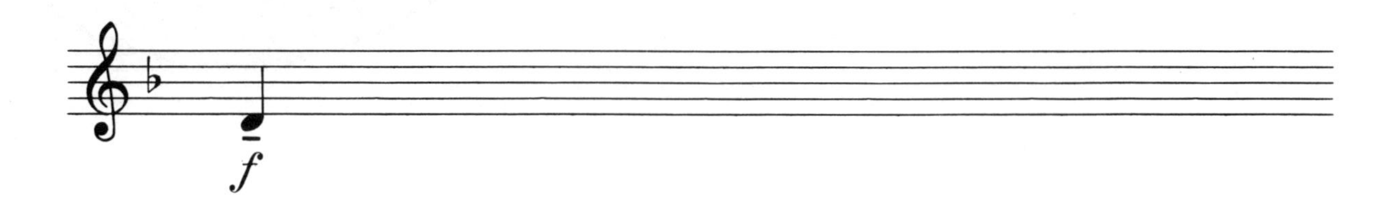

Exercise 35 This is the beginning of a melody from a piano piece ('Last Saturday Evening') by Grieg. Look at it and then answer the questions below.

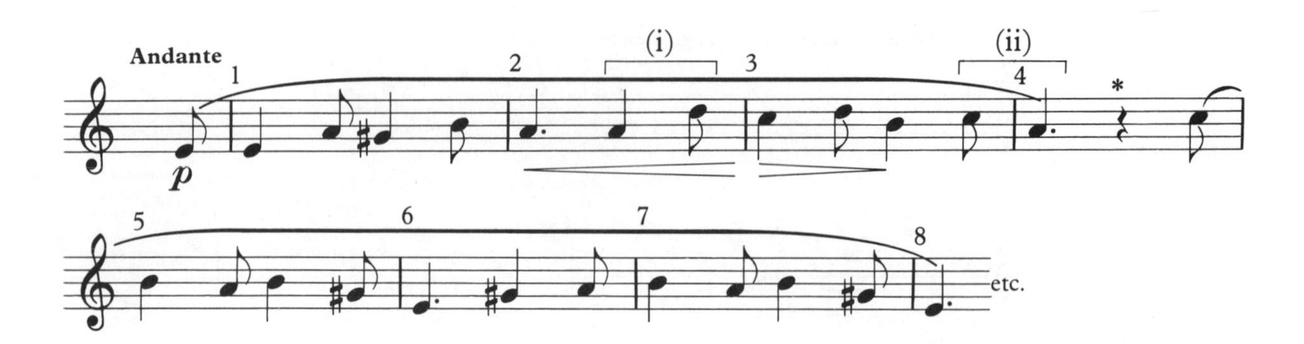

(a) What is the key? ....

(b) Add the time signature where required.

(c) Name the two intervals marked (i) and (ii).
(i) .... (ii) ....

(d) Give the meaning of:
(i) **Andante** ....
(ii) *p* ....

(e) Give the degree of the scale of the first note ....

(f) Where is the music loudest? ....

(g) There are two long slurs over the notes: from the beginning to bar 4, and from bar 4 to the end. What do they mean? ....

(h) What do the two sections of the melody, marked by these two slurs, have in common?
....

(i) Starting at * (in bar 4), rewrite the music in simple time, beginning as shown.

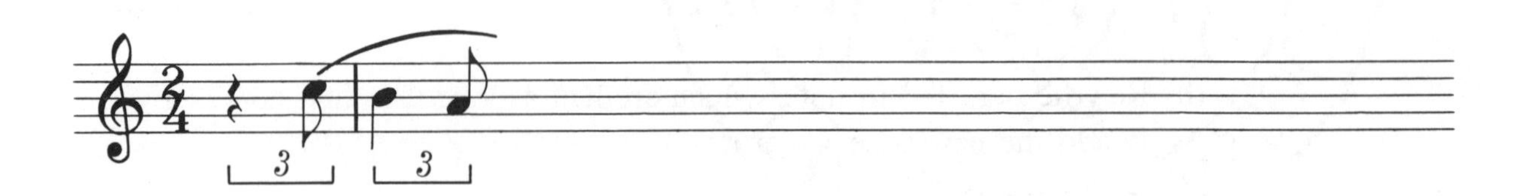